KU-335-040

Dear Girls and Boys,

I'm sure you will enjoy reading this bright and colourful **BIMBO BOOK**. Inside, there are lots of super stories like Arnie the flying Aardvark and Bobbity's whiskers. Bumpy Bonzo, Pip Penguin You will find comic adventures with and Flipperfeet, to enjoy, too. There are also Puzzles to do and an exciting shopping game to play.

Bye-Bye for now

Bimbo

Wonderland

The Painted Lady butterflies
Give tawny wings a flick.
"Shall I chase one?" the weasel thinks.
But they are much too quick!

These dormice play at hide-and-seek,
About their grassy nest.
They'll curl up each and go to sleep.
They like a lot of rest.

Up from their earthy burrow home,
Two fox cubs look around.
How wonderful the wide world seems,
When you've been underground!

Now turn to the back of the book.

Printed and Published by D. C. Thomson & Co., Ltd., Dundee and London.

Trumpalot

TRUMPALOT, the elephant, was very excited. King Leopold the Second was coming to visit his village! All the animals had a meeting to decide what they would do on the great day.

"Well," said the chimp, "I think we should give an acrobatic display."

"How about a swimming display?" said a pretty little flamingo.

"And we will sing a very special song for his majesty," said one of the birds.

"What about a display of dancing?" hissed the snake.

"*We* shall form a very special guard of honour in the water, and salute his majesty as he passes by!" snapped a big crocodile.

For weeks, the animals practised — and got in each other's way. One of the swinging Chimpanzees even knocked Snappy, the crocodile, into the water!

The only one who had nothing to say was Trumpalot. He simply trotted off into the jungle each morning and returned later, looking very pleased with himself.

Pokey, the nosey ant-eater, tried to follow Trumpalot one day. But his legs were not as long as those of his big, grey friend, and he soon lost him among the trees.

Finally, the day came when King Leopold was due to arrive.

"He's on his way," panted Cheetah, the look-out. Quickly, the animals rushed to take up their places. The crocodiles got ready to salute, while the birds cleared their throats to sing. The flamingos formed a circle in the water to begin their water ballet.

Monkeys and chimpanzees balanced in a pyramid and the snakes waited in the middle to begin their dance.

The animals had forgotten about Trumpalot, and were very surprised to see him walk shyly into the clearing.

They were even more surprised when, as the king approached, Trumpalot raised his head and, pointing his trunk to the sky, trumpeted a tremendous fanfare!

Trumpalot blew so hard that the birds were blown off the trees, the crocodiles dived for cover and the chimpanzees tumbled like a pack of cards.

King Leopold called the little elephant to his side. "I'm *very* sorry, Your Majesty," Trumpalot said. "I didn't mean to spoil everything."

"I haven't laughed so much in years!" cried the king. "Come and sit with me, my funny friend, and we'll watch the display together!" Trumpalot felt *so* proud.

The gentle grouse

HER feathers are a dark red-brown.
  She wears fine combs above her eyes.
You'll find her on the windswept moors,
  Where day and night the curlew cries.

Around mauve-heathered slopes she'll search
  For bilberries she likes to eat.
Then, pass a vole with orange teeth,
  Exploring on the boggy peat.

She'll spy a bee who stops to sip
  The nectar from a harebell there,
And then a fox who's peering round
  The stack of stones he's made his lair.

She watches golden eagles as
  These great birds glide across the sky,
To land close to their hidden nest,
  Upon a rocky ledge so high.

In sheltered bracken she will rest,
  As antlered, red deer stags walk past,
Until a brown-furred mountain hare
  Speeds on his journey, oh, so fast.

Bumpy Bonzo

BONZO was such a clumsy dog that all the other animals on the farm laughed at him and called him Bumpy Bonzo. He had great, big paws and was always bumping into things and knocking them over.

Most of the time, Bonzo lived in a kennel outside. And it was just as well, too, for, when he went into the farmhouse, he wagged his long, shaggy tail so hard that all the cups were knocked off the table.

Bonzo was very fond of Heidi's puppies. They were red setters and there were ten of them. But, when he licked them, Bonzo rolled them over so hard that they cried out and Heidi grew cross.

Bonzo wanted to make himself useful on the farm, so he went to the barn, where he met Blackie, the retriever.

"Where are you going?" he asked him.

"I am going to the hen house to collect some eggs," answered Blackie.

"Can I come and help?" said Bonzo.

"Of course you can," answered Blackie, who was a very kind old dog. He helped Mrs Jones gather the eggs in the hen house.

But, when Bonzo tried to roll the eggs across the straw like Blackie, the eggs cracked and broke.

"I *am* sorry," said Bonzo. "Shall I try again?"

"No," sighed Blackie, trying to be kind. "You are so big and strong that you cannot help breaking them."

As Bonzo went back to his kennel, the hens cackled at him, "Poor Bumpy Bonzo. He can't even roll an egg without breaking it!"

One day, there was a blizzard. Mr Jones was very worried as his tractor was buried in snow, and he couldn't think how to carry the hay to the sheep in the fields.

Then Mrs Jones had an idea. "Why don't you take that big sledge from the shed?" she called. "You could load it up with hay and we could harness Bonzo to it. He is the only dog strong enough to pull it!"

So, all that day, Bonzo pulled the sledge filled with hay up the field to the sheep.

"*Baa, baa*!" cried the sheep. "We will call you *Brave Bonzo* after this!"

Afterwards, Mr Jones put a bucket of barley and another bucket of fresh water on the sledge. Bonzo was feeling very tired by then, but he pulled the heavy sledge one more time. The hens were pleased to see him.

"How strong you are, Bonzo!" they clucked as they ate their supper and had a drink. "Our own water is frozen solid."

None of the animals ever called him Bumpy Bonzo again!

"You are a very good dog!" said Mr Jones, giving him a specially nice supper and a big, juicy bone!

Jungle play-time

There are six tents hidden on this page. Can you find them?

Join the dots to see what kind of animal the explorers have spotted.

Find your way through the maze to catch Gerry Giraffe.

Can you tell which of these two bush babies are exactly alike?

Which of these is the odd one out? Answer: The penguin. The others live in the jungle.

Try to spot six differences between these two elephants.

Gerry Giraffe's good deed

1 — Gerry Giraffe felt silly. For the first time in his life, he had seen a reflection of himself in the jungle pool. He thought he looked very strange.

2 — "Look at my thin, spindly legs, and my long neck!" he wailed. "*You* don't look any funnier than we do," said the zebras. "Or us!" added a monkey.

3 — Then, one day, while Gerry was reaching up for some tasty leaves high in a tree, he caught sight of a herd of charging elephants.

4 — Gerry warned his jungle chums, who quickly ran away to safety. They knew that if anyone got in the elephants' way, they would be trampled by their heavy feet.

5 — Suddenly, Gerry heard someone crying. "What will *we* do, Gerry?" sobbed a little mouse. "We can't run away as fast as the bigger animals."

6 — Gerry knew just what to do. He bent down his long neck and told the smaller animals to climb up on his head. Then he gently lifted them on to a tall tree.

7 — Gerry helped all the little animals to safety that way. The last to go was a family of beetles. How they tickled as they scampered over Gerry's nose!

8 — No sooner had Gerry rescued all the beetles, than the runaway elephants came charging by. Gerry gasped, "Luckily, everyone is out of their way."

9 — After the elephants had gone, Gerry lifted the little animals back down. "Thanks, Gerry!" cried the mouse. "Your long legs and neck are really useful."

10 — After that, Gerry often let his chums slide down his neck while he reached up for tasty leaves. Only a giraffe could do that, and there was nothing Gerry would rather be!

Our happy snowman

WE made our snowman after school.
He stands there where the wall is low,
And everybody smiles at him.
The milkman even says, "Hello!"

His eyes and teeth are made of coal,
His scarf is long, and brightest red,
And, sometimes, birds perch on his pipe
To eat their tasty crumbs of bread!

I wished that he could play with us
At snowball fights, or on my sleigh.
But all he did was stand and smile
And watch the snowflakes fall all day.

Our dog thought he was real, but strange.
He'd bark, then run away to hide!
But now, he's quite his newest friend,
And likes to sit down by his side!

We think the snow is melting, though.
It's dropping down from every bough.
But, wait! It's snowing once again!
Hurrah! We'll keep our snowman now!

Hector's happy birthday

1 — It was Hector Hedgehog's birthday. "I'm going to do something exciting," the little hedgehog said. "Don't go wandering away," warned his mother.

2 — Hector promised to be back in time for tea. "I think I'll do some exploring first," thought the wee hedgehog. "That garden looks very interesting to me."

3 — Hector had never been out on his own before and he found the garden was full of things to look at. Suddenly, he saw some tasty strawberries.

4 — "They look good," thought Hector. "I'll try a few." So the hedgehog began to tuck in. But Hector hadn't noticed a net which was covering the strawberries.

5 — The farther Hector went into the strawberry patch, the more he became tangled up in the net. "Oh, no!" gasped the little hedgehog. "What will I do?"

6 — Hector struggled and wriggled, but it was no good. He couldn't get out of that net. At last, the tired, little hedgehog rolled up and went to sleep.

7 — Hector dozed until he heard a girl calling. "Look, Mummy!" she cried. "There's a prickly ball in our garden." The girl's mum began to laugh.

8 — "That's not a prickly ball," she said. "It's a hedgehog and he's all tangled up in our strawberry net. I'll fetch my scissors and cut him free."

9 — Carefully the girl's mother cut away the net. "There," she said. "That didn't take long. Now I expect this little chap is wanting something to eat."

10 — She fetched some bread and milk. "Can I keep him?" asked the girl. "No," replied her mother. "It's kinder to let him go back to his own family."

11 — After Hector had eaten his tasty meal, he hurried off to his home. "Hello, Mum and Dad! I'm back from my adventure!" called young Hector.

12 — "Tell us all about it," said Dad. And that's just what Hector did. "You *have* had an exciting birthday," smiled Mum. "But now it's time for bed!"

Buzz-bee and the butterfly bush

1 — Buzz-bee and his friend, Bob, were gathering nectar from the flowers of a large rhododendron bush when some bees from another hive arrived.

2 — "Hey! Buzz off, you!" the fierce bees cried. "This bush is ours now!" Buzz and Bob didn't stop to argue. They flew to the other side of the garden.

3 — Buzz watched miserably as the greedy bees gorged themselves on the big flower bush. "There are only a few dandelions left for us," he sighed.

4 — When Buzz and Bob returned without any nectar, the baby bees in the nursery started to cry. "This is awful!" groaned Buzz. "I must do *something*."

5 — So, that evening, when all the other bees were asleep, Buzz crept out to visit some of his butterfly friends. "Perhaps they can help," he thought.

6 — Next morning, Buzz told all the bees to stay inside. "We will soon have plenty of food for the babies," he said. Everybody waited and watched.

7 — The greedy bees came again, but then they suddenly flew away in a swarm to a far corner of the garden. "Right!" cried Buzz. "Come on."

8 — As they gathered nectar from the rhododendron bush, however, Bob grew curious. "Where did these greedy bees go?" he asked. "Look!" giggled Buzz.

9 — The greedy bees were hovering around what looked like a beautiful bush with masses of white and yellow blooms. But they were buzzing angrily. For they realised they'd been tricked! The flowers weren't flowers at all, but Buzz's friends, the butterflies, who had gathered on an old tree stump to make it look like a flower bush!

10 — After that, all the bees agreed to share the big rhododendron bush, for there was plenty of nectar to feed everyone. "Well done, Buzz Bee," said the Queen Bee. "You've saved the hive." "I couldn't have done it without the butterflies!" laughed Buzz.

Little Olly
lends a hand

DEEP down, at the bottom of the ocean, King and Queen Octopus were having breakfast. "I've been thinking, my dear," said the king. "Let's have a dance for your birthday."

"What a *lovely* idea!" cried the queen. "I'll write the invitations at once. We have such a lot of friends and my birthday is only two weeks away."

The king's grandson, Olly, had been listening. "Who's going to play the music for dancing?" he asked.

"We'll ask the Four Fish Fingers," the king said, with a smile. "They're your favourite group, aren't they?"

Olly was *delighted*. He thought the Fish Fingers were marvellous and spent hours practising, trying to sound just like them. And now they were coming to the palace.

"Wait till my friends hear about this!" cried Olly, before dashing off to his room for even *more* practice!

On the day of the dance, there was great hustle and bustle in the palace. "Can I help prepare the food?" Olly asked the cook. "No, thank you," she said. "I've got all the help I need."

Olly went to look for his grandmother. "Do *you* need any help?" he asked. "No, dear," she sighed. "I'm afraid you would only get in my way. Why don't you go and have a ride on one of the palace seahorses?"

Olly didn't want to ride, so he went into the ballroom where his grandfather was putting up the decorations. "Now, don't touch anything," called the king before Olly could say a word. "Just go and play, like a good boy."

"I wish I could do *something* to help," sighed Olly, as he went outside.

At last, everything was ready. The tables were laden with all kinds of delicious things to eat and the decorations in the ballroom were simply splendid. Before long, the guests started to arrive — fishes of all colours and sizes, crabs, lobsters and shrimps — but there was no sign of the Four Fish Fingers.

"I wish they would hurry up," the king whispered to the queen. "I'm beginning to get worried!" Suddenly, a messenger rushed in.

"The Sea Shell Coach has broken down," he puffed. "The Fish Fingers can't get here tonight."

"Oh, no," groaned the king. "The evening is ruined. How can we have a dance without music?"

But Olly had an idea and he hurried off to his room.

A few minutes later, Olly arrived back in the ballroom with a guitar, a drum kit, a mouth organ and a xylophone. "Goodness gracious me!" exclaimed the king.

"It's all right, grandfather," said Olly. "I've been practising hard and I know all the Four Fish Fingers' songs." So Olly played for the guests and everyone had a marvellous time.

At bed-time, Olly's grandmother came to say goodnight. "Thank you for my lovely birthday music," she said. Olly was very happy. "I'm glad I was able to help after all," he said, with a *very* sleepy smile.

Perry's magic hat

1 — The squirrels who lived in South Wood were growing very annoyed. "Where *can* our acorns be?" grumbled one. "I'm *so* hungry."

2 — Just then, a squirrel looked behind a tree. "It's Perry the Pixie!" he cried. "You've been up to mischief again. Where have you hidden our acorns *this* time?"

3 — Perry was *always* upsetting the animals. You see, when he put on his magic hat, he became invisible and the animals couldn't see him playing tricks!

4 — The animals decided to do something about this cheeky pixie. "Let's swop his magic hat for an ordinary one," twittered a robin. "That should be fun!"

5 — Everyone agreed to the plan. When Perry fell asleep, a little shrew crept up and changed the hats. "Let's see what happens, now!" she chuckled.

6 — Next morning, Perry thought he would play some tricks as usual. Thinking he was invisible, he crept up to a blackbird and reached for some crumbs.

7 — "Get your own crumbs!" the blackbird croaked crossly, and gave Perry a sharp peck. "How can you see me?" Perry gasped. "I've got my hat on!"

8 — The animals laughed to see Perry being taught a lesson. But then, two children came along and found Perry. "Let's take him home," said the girl.

9 — So, Perry was put in a rabbit hutch while the children went to fetch their father. The animals felt sorry for him. "Oh, dear!" wailed the shrew.

10 — "We must rescue Perry," said the blackbird, and he flew over to the rabbit hutch with the pixie's magic hat. "Thank you," said Perry, gratefully.

11 — Then the blackbird unlocked the hutch and Perry slipped out. Quickly, the pixie fastened the catch again and ran for the safety of the long grass.

12 — "But we *did* have a pixie in the hutch, Dad," puzzled the boy. "Thanks chums," said Perry. "I'll never play tricks on you again — well, *almost* never!"

The cheery chaffinch

THE chaffinch is a cheery bird.
He dresses smartly, too!
His waistcoat is a rosy pink.
His cap is shiny blue.

When sunny, summer days are here,
I love to see him come
Hop-hopping round, at picnic time,
To peck up every crumb.

And, in the golden autumn months,
Fat berries are his treat.
He flits along the lane to find
A tasty one to eat.

"Pink! Pink!" I hear him pipe, upon
The elderberry tree,
One bright eye on the berries black,
And one bright eye on me!

Playroom puzzle-time

Use your paints or crayons to colour in these pictures of the animals having fun. Then try to find six toy cars hidden on these pages.

Join the dots to see what Kitty and Henry are playing with.

Which of these yo-yos is Marty holding?

Answer: — B.

here are six differences between these two pictures. Can you spot them?

Can you tell which two of these counting frames is exactly alike?

scramble the letters to find the names of these books.

Help Bernie through the maze to reach his paints.

HTE
RHEET
TILETL
GPSI

SUSP
NI
SOBTO

Minnie's big adventure

MINNIE the minnow was a little fish who lived in a tiny pond. But she didn't like it there at all. She wanted to swim in a big, big river. The other pond creatures laughed when Minnie swam around with her nose in the air, pretending to be a big fish.

"A small pond may be all right for *you*," Minnie sniffed, "but I want adventure. This little pond is *much* too boring!"

Then, one day, it started raining heavily and the water in the pond began to rise.

"We'd better find shelter!" cried the pond creatures. "Are you coming, Minnie?"

"No," replied the minnow. "I *like* the pond this way — it's more exciting."

The rain began to fall even heavier, but Minnie kept on swimming around the pond.

Later that morning, it was still raining and the pond water was getting very deep and rough. Even the ducks were beginning to get worried.

"Come with us, Minnie!" they quacked. "We'll have to go somewhere safe. The pond is about to burst its banks!"

But Minnie wouldn't listen. "Don't let me stop you," she sniffed.

The ducks shrugged their wings. "You're being very silly," they called.

Minnie swam about the empty pond quite happily.

"Imagine those silly creatures being frightened of a little rain," she laughed. But then, suddenly, the heavy rain made the pond burst its banks and the water started to spill over on to the fields.

As the pond water began to swirl faster and faster, Minnie found she wasn't strong enough to swim against it.

"Oh, dear!" she wailed. "This isn't the kind of adventure I wanted at all."

The waves carried Minnie along in their path and she could only flap her fins feebly as she fought against the rush of icy water.

Minnie was soon completely tired out. She was just about to be swept off, when, luckily, she became tangled up in a cluster of weeds. "I'm saved!" she gasped.

"I wish the pond was nice and peaceful again," she sighed later. "If only I had listened to what the others said."

After the rain finally stopped, Minnie's friends came back to look for her.

"Here she is!" called the frog. And, quickly, everyone hurried over to help untangle Minnie.

"Now you know you should have come with us," fussed the ducks. "You're lucky just to have a bruised fin!"

"I know," said Minnie. "I was a very foolish minnow. But I've learned my lesson. I'll be quite happy to be a little fish in a little pond from now on!"

Camping puzzles

Comp MENU
enasB. Tae.
oupS
Fh.s. jma.
jlely.

Help Timmy through the maze to reach the water tap.

Rearrange the letters to find out what the campers are having for lunch, then colour this picture with your paints. Answer:—
Beans, Tea, Soup, Fish, Jam and Jelly.

Join the dots to see what this is.

Which of these tent ropes is tied to the tent?
Answer:— B.

Can you tell which two of these logs are exactly alike?

There are six flags hidden on this page. Can you find them?

1 — Santa Claus was looking upset when Pip m
him just before Christmas. "Why aren't y
delivering these presents?" asked Pip.

4 — "The seagulls can carry the children's presents to Eskimo Town," Pip chuckled. "Just watch."

5 — The presents were too heavy for th little gulls, however. They flopped to th ground with a *bump* and a *squawk*

8 — "We'll never get the toys delivered," wailed Santa. "It's a shame."

9 — "Wait, there's somebody I've forgotte about!" Pip cried. "Just push the sleigh int the sea and he'll take us all to Eskimo Town.

— "My reindeer have colds," sighed Santa. "They're not well enough to pull the sleigh to town this morning!"

3 — "I've a super idea!" cried Pip. "I'll ask my seagull chums to help. Come on! Over here quickly, lads."

— Pip's next idea was to ask Pete, the polar bear, to pull Santa's sleigh to Eskimo Town.

7 — Pete took off at a gallop. But he ran too fast and the presents were all shaken out. "Stop! Come back!" cried Pip.

— Santa and Pip rode to Eskimo Town on Wally the whale. "Yippee! Hooray for Santa and Pip!" cheered the children.

See how fast you can, go
Shopping for Gran

To play this game, all you need is a dice and the little rabbit counters shown on the right.

Cut them out and paste them on to cardboard. Throw a six to start, then, next throw, off you go.

The first player to collect Granny's shopping and take it to her is the winner.

Start

1

2

Mr Badger gives you flowers for Gran. Go on 4 places. **3**

4

5

The squirrel twins switch the path sign. Miss a turn. **6**

7

8

9

Freddie Fox steals a cake from your shopping trolley. Run back 3 places to chase him. **10**

11

12

13 You find Mr Hedgehog's hat and he gives you a fish for Gran. Go on to 18.

14

15

21

22

23
You join the dormouse family for a picnic. Miss a turn.

24

You drop your shopping list. Go back 4 places to find it.
19

20

25

18

27
Your shopping trolley rolls down a hill. Run back to 20 to fetch it.

26

17

Finish

28

Mrs Hare shows you a short-cut through the wood. Go straight to 28.
16

31

29

30

Flipperfeet learns to swim

FLIPPERFEET, the turtle, was busy sunning himself on a rock watching his chums swim in the cool river. He thought how nice it would be if he could join them. But poor Flipperfeet just couldn't swim. He had tried, of course, but it was no use.

Every time he jumped into the water, he sank to the bottom. The other turtles knew this and left Flipperfeet to watch safely from the water's edge. However, there was one turtle called Terry, who always teased Flipperfeet.

"Why don't you come on into the water, Flipperfeet!" called a cheeky voice. It was Terry again! "The water's lovely. It's a pity *you* can't swim!"

Just then, Flipperfeet's friend, Tina, swam over.

2 — "I can give you swimming lessons," said Tina. "You'll soon learn to swim."

Then Terry appeared. "Don't waste your time on him, Tina," scoffed the turtle, and he pushed Tina under the water!

Poor Tina was so surprised at being ducked under, that she could hardly swim to the river bank. Well, when Flipperfeet saw what a fright Tina had got, he was very angry. And, without stopping to think, he slid off the rock . . .

3 — . . . and landed right on top of Terry. "That'll teach him not to bully my friends," thought Flipperfeet angrily. He looked around to see if Tina was all right . . . and was surprised to see her laughing.

"Look, Flipperfeet!" she called. "You're *swimming*!"

"You're right!" he cried. "I was so angry I just jumped in and began to swim. Come and see me, everybody. I can swim at last. I won't need swimming lessons after all."

And all the other turtles gathered round to cheer Flipperfeet. Even cheeky Terry joined in and clapped his flippers.

Arnie the *flying* Aardvark

1 — Arnie was a little aardvark who lived with his parents in a burrow somewhere in Africa. Arnie's hobby was adventure collecting. He just loved adventures!

2 — One night, when Arnie wandered away from his burrow, he saw some very strange objects. They were tents, but Arnie didn't know that, of course.

3 — Deciding to explore, Arnie saw all sorts of interesting things. Then, suddenly, he tripped over a guy rope — and one of the things fell on top of him!

4 — As Arnie stood, covered in flour, a man leapt up from a bunk and switched on a torch. "It's a baby aardvark!" he cried. "Catch it, someone!"

5 — Before Arnie could run away, a box was dropped over him. He had a horrible feeling that, unless he escaped, he might never see his family again.

6 — The aardvark had never dug so fast in his life before. But soon he was free again and running off as fast as his little legs would carry him.

7 — When Arnie stopped, however, he realised he was lost. "Can you help me?" Arnie asked Jambi, the nightjar. "Wait there, little fellow," called the bird.

8 — Arnie waited and waited, then, suddenly, he found himself being lifted off the ground and high into the air.

9 — "I'm Boreo, the eagle," said a voice. "I know where *everyone* lives. And I'll make sure you won't leave a trail for those hunters to follow," he continued.

10 — At first, Arnie was frightened. But then he gasped with delight. "No aardvark has ever been as high as this before. It's beautiful up here!" he cried.

11 — Boreo knew exactly where Arnie's family lived and he set him down right by his door. "Wait till you hear where *I've* been!" Arnie called to his mum.

12 — Later, tucked up in bed, Arnie settled down to dream about his adventure. "Today I became the world's first ever *flying* aardvark!" he sighed.

Happy

I CALL my hamster Happy, as
  He's such a merry fellow.
His eyes are bright as blackberries.
  His fur is brownish yellow.

He has a sturdy wooden cage,
  With sawdust on the floor,
And there's a ladder that he climbs
  To reach his bedroom door.

Inside, he makes a cosy nest.
  He likes to sleep all day.
Then, when it is *my* supper time,
  He hurries out to play.

He races round and round his wheel,
  And never once looks back,
Then comes and sits upon my hand
  To eat a tasty snack.

I take great care of Happy, for
  I love him so, you see,
And from the look in his bright eyes,
  I think that he loves me!

Loopy's lost voice

1 — Loopy the snake sneezed loudly, just as Gracie Gazelle passed near his tree. "I seem to have caught this dreadful cold," sniffed Loopy. "I can't stop sneezing."

2 — "Do you feel shivery?" asked Gracie. "Is your throat sore?" The snake swallowed painfully. "Very sore," he croaked. "And I've such a *long* throat."

3 — "Listen, Loopy," said the kind gazelle. "Coil up on your branch and keep warm. I'll ask Mrs Chimp to bring you something to make you well."

4 — Although Mrs Chimp's medicine tasted awful, she soon had Loopy feeling better. Though now that his throat no longer hurt, his voice had disappeared!

5 — All Loopy's friends offered advice, but nothing would bring back his lost voice. "I'll just lie in the sun," sighed Loopy. "Perhaps it will make me better!"

6 — The day was hot and Loopy soon fell fast asleep in his tree. That was why he didn't hear the *thump! thump! thump!* of the marching elephant herd.

7 — Nearer and nearer came the herd, trumpeting a marching song and beating time with their tails. Their leader, Elmer, marched before them with his head high.

8 — Elmer was too busy trumpeting and marching to notice the snoozing snake's long tail trailing across the ground in front of him. His big foot came down . . .

9 — . . . right on Loopy's tail. "Yee-ow!" howled the startled snake. "That hurts!" Loopy leaped into the air, then fell, with a *bump* at Elmer's feet.

10 — "Oops! I'm for it now," gasped Elmer. But, instead of shouting angrily, Loopy smiled, for he suddenly realised the shock had brought his voice back!

11 — "Ho! Ho! I think your sore throat has slipped all the way to your tail," laughed Mrs Chimp when she saw Loopy. "What a silly snake you are."

The king of the birds

1 — Once upon a time, all the birds of the air agreed to hold a meeting. They swooped down together into a large wood. "Why are we here?" chirped a tiny wren.

2 — "We have decided," twittered a sparrow, "to choose a king." All the birds thought that was a good idea. "Who will *be* king?" they asked.

3 — A large and haughty eagle puffed himself up and began to speak. "Why, *I* shall be king," he said. "I am the biggest and most powerful of all the birds."

4 — "But you live in the mountains," piped a goldcrest. "I live in town gardens and the countryside. I can see everything that's going on."

5 — "Let's have a contest to see who can fly the highest!" cried another bird. "Whoever can will see the farthest and so be king of the birds."

6 — The birds all happily agreed to that, except the tiny goldcrest. "That's me out of the contest," he sighed. "The other birds can fly higher than I can. Unless . . ."

7 — "Ho! Ho!" jeered the blackbird, as he flew off above the trees. "The goldcrest knows he's beaten already."

8 — The contest began. Soon, the smaller birds were left far below and the larger ones flew higher and higher. "Look!" called the tiny wren. "The eagle and the buzzard have flown the highest."

9 — The two birds of prey flew higher still. "You'll have to give in, buzzard!" cried the eagle. "You know I can fly far higher than you." And with that, he *did*!

10 — Suddenly, from among the thick feathers on the eagle's back, the little goldcrest appeared! He had hidden there, knowing it was his only chance!

11 — As the goldcrest flew up, the poor eagle was too tired to follow. "I am the highest!" sang the tiny bird. "The goldcrest *deserves* to win!" cried the sparrow.

12 — And so the goldcrest was crowned king of the birds. Although he wasn't the biggest, he was certainly the cleverest of them all!

Darren's busy day

ONE morning, Darren Dormouse heard someone running up and down the river-bank. He poked his head outside. "Why, Mrs Shrew! Whatever's the matter?" he gasped. "Oh, Darren, please help me!" cried Mrs Shrew.

"The bridge is broken and I can't get over the stream to my family."

2 — "Don't worry," replied Darren. "Let's see if Wally Wagtail can help." But Wally just shook his head. "I'm sorry, Mrs Shrew," he said. "I would fly you across, but you're too heavy. Why don't you ask Morris Mole for help. He lives farther up the path. Perhaps he could dig you a tunnel."

3 — The two friends hurried along to Morris Mole's house. "Can you dig a tunnel for us under the stream?" asked Darren. "Oh, no!" cried Morris. "That's *much* too dangerous." Mrs Shrew was very upset.

4 — But Thomas Toad had been listening. "I think *I* can help," he offered. "How?" asked Mrs Shrew. "Well," replied Thomas, "I can carry you across the stream on my back — I'm a good swimmer, you know!"

So, they did just that and soon Mrs Shrew reached her family, safe and sound.

"Now," yawned Darren, "perhaps I can go and catch up on my sleep!"

The Garden Folk

Freddy Frog is easy to make. Cut out the body shape, arms and legs like this.

Fold the body along the dotted line and paint the inside of the "mouth" red.

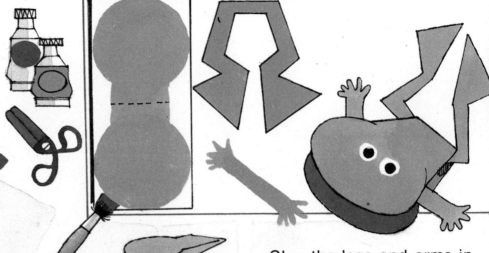

Glue the legs and arms in place, add eyes and there you have Freddy!

Now you can make Freddy's chum, Sammy Snail.

Cut two strips of cardboard, one longer than the other, like this. Cut a V shape into one end of the shorter strip to make two points.

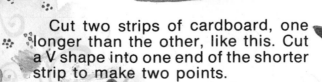

Coil the longer strip, then fold the end of the short length over and stick the coil into it. Add a cheery face and meet Sammy!

All the garden folk love flowers. You can make some to decorate a garden for them.

Use your paints or crayons to make coloured tissue paper circles.

Then simply glue different ones together on to lolly sticks to form lots of brightly coloured "flowers".

Herbie Hedgehog is made out of a potato. To give him spines and legs, make holes in the potato and stick drinking straws into them.

There are lots of things-to-do and stories and puzzles, too, in "Twinkle", the picture paper specially for little girls. On sale every Wednesday.

To make Birdie, cut out the body and wings like this, and fold along the dotted lines. Glue the wings inside the folded body. Lastly, glue on string legs and card triangles for feet.

Panto puzzles

You can use your paints or crayons to colour this picture of the animals' "Dick Whittington" panto.

Help Cinderella through the maze to her coach.

Unscramble the jumbled up letters to learn the name of this panto.

KACJ
NAD HET
LBSAKTNEA

Try to spot six differences between these two pictures.

There are six panto tickets hidden on this page. Can you find them?

Bobbity's whiskers

1 — Bobbity Rabbit was very proud of his long whiskers. "No one has a finer set," he thought, as he set off for his usual morning walk round the garden.

2 — Then, Bobbity noticed his neighbour, Herbie Hedgehog, working busily in the garden. "I wonder what he's doing?" thought Bobbity, curiously.

3 — Bobbity couldn't help taking a look. But, when he leaned on the fence, it gave way under his weight! Poor Bobbity almost fell on top of Herbie's bonfire!

4 — "Are you all right?" Herbie exclaimed. "Yes," sniffed Bobbity. "But I'm all dusty!" "You *must* be fine, if that's all you're worried about," Herbie said.

5 — As Herbie brushed Bobbity's suit, however, he gasped, "The bonfire has singed your whiskers !" "Oh, no!" Bobbity wailed and he ran off howling.

6 — Later, Herbie found Bobbity at home with a scarf round his face. "This special cream is to make your whiskers grow," said Herbie. But nothing happened.

7 — Next morning, Herbie called at Bobbity's house again. "Come on!" he called. "I've heard of a little shop which sells everything — even whiskers!"

8 — In the shop, the goblin shopkeeper showed Bobbity all kinds of whiskers. "I'll take those green ones," said Bobbity. "They match my suit exactly!"

9 — "You will need green thread," said the goblin. "Why?" asked Bobbity. "To sew your whiskers on," explained the goblin. "Not likely!" cried Bobbity.

10 — "The goblin was joking," giggled Herbie, when he caught up with Bobbity. "Look in the mirror." Bobbity did. "My whiskers have grown again!" he cried.

11 — "And they're finer than before!" laughed Bobbity, doing a dance around the garden. "I must invite everyone to a party to show them off!" "Ho! Ho!" chuckled Herbie. "Good old Bobbity!"

The squirrel is a cheeky chap,
With bushy tail all red.
He fills his larder full of nuts,
For winter days ahead.

Hush! If you tip-toe in the woods,
And don't make any noise,
You might catch these wee mice at play.
The same as girls and boys!

Here's Mrs Stoat with all her babes.
She has a *lot* to do.
Her little ones are full of fun,
But can be naughty, too!